Inside this little book
is a world of magical and funny
imaginary animals
from A to Z.

An amberhook
looks like a frog, but has an
amber-colored hooked tail,
large pointy teeth,
and sharp claws.
An amberhook's bulging
eyes pop out of its head
when its prey is near.

A is for amberhook.

Ballyfeet are purple.
They have tiny epidgeal
legs, but they
don't touch
the ground.
They only have one eye.

B is for ballyfeet.

Cominga is a
camel-like creature,
but its hump is
underneath, and
it has a pointy
anteater nose.

C is for cominga.

A dodanddoo
is a tripod.
The female has
flashy red wings.

D is for dodanddoo.

An elloderm
has many skin folds.
It looks like a deflated
beanbag. It has two large
tusks on each side
of its head.
The elloderm sings
gorgeous songs.

E is for elloderm.

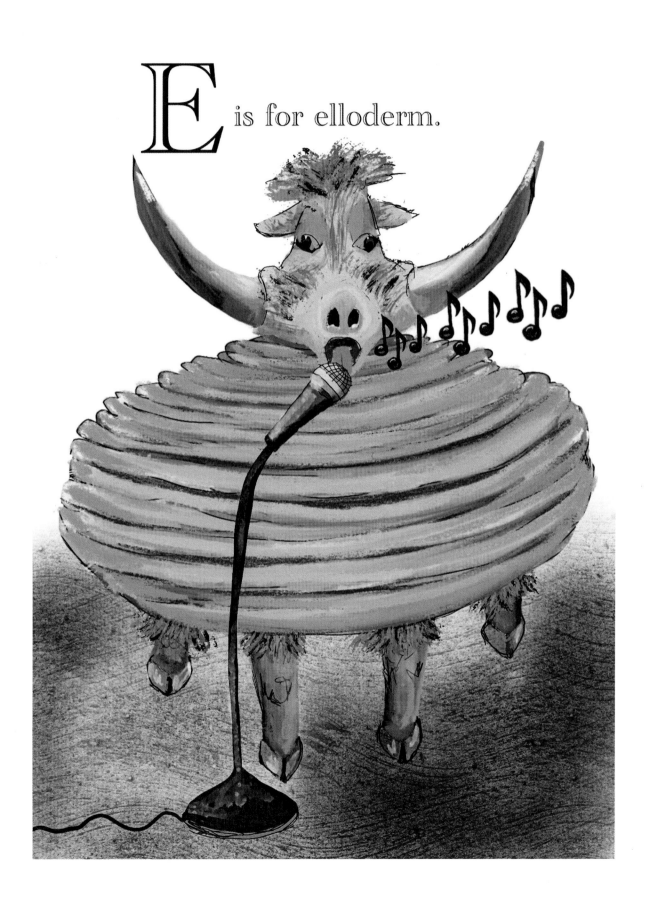

A farsel is a
half robot
hybrid peacock.
The tail is
animatronic,
and it moves
quickly on
spring-like legs.

F is for farsel.

A gnarsplint
is a small mammal
with enormous eyes
like a tarsier.
It has six appendages with
three fingers
on each.
It lives in thorn bushes,
which is a liability given its big
beautiful eyes.

G is for gnarsplint.

Harvingas are
Mexican leaf bugs. They
look like maple tree seeds,
and descend like
drifting helicopters.
They have small antennae
on their heads,
and are fun
to watch fall.

H is for harvingas.

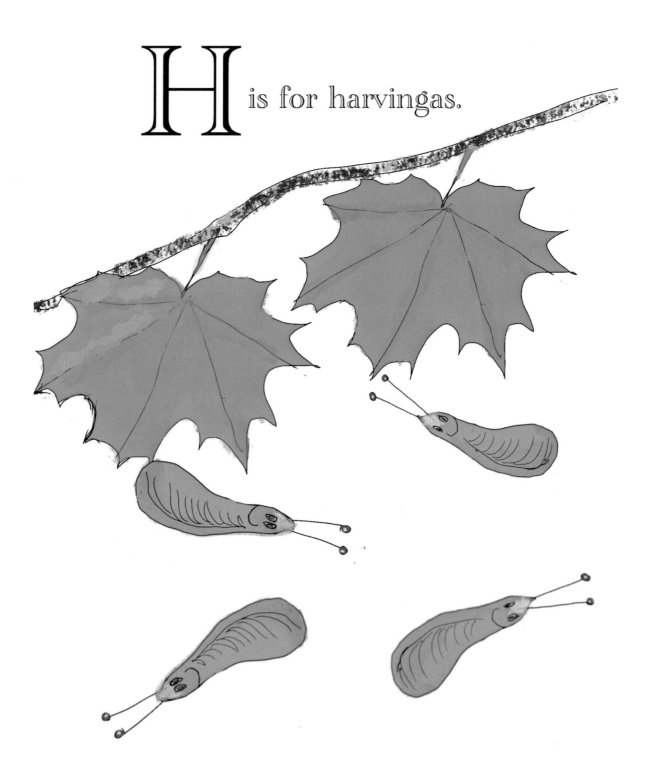

Ichanthia are
small tube worms shaped
like candy corn.
They have a corkscrew type
web around them.
They live in hydrothermal
vents, and burp up little
smoke rings.

I is for ichanthia.

A jojoja
is a pretty fur ball.
Cute like a hamster, until it
smiles. Then you see its ugly
conical teeth
that look similar
to an opossum's.
It has a Mohawk that
lays to one side
like a horses's mane.

J is for jojoja.

A kalliwhop
has the appearance
of an alligator
with no torso.
It has a large long head
and a beaver-like tail.
It lives in the mud,
and eats frogs.

K is for kalliwhop.

A llark, pronounced
yark, is a six-foot tall
creature that
walks on its toes.
The llark is related to
the dolphin, but has a
tail instead
of a dorsal fin.
It evolved to
traverse on land.

L is for llark.

A miln is similar
to a walking stick,
but it actually
is more of a log.
Other woodland
plants and animals make a
miln their habitat, unaware
they're on a living critter.

M is for miln.

A nottle is peculiar in the
animal kingdom;
it appears to wear glasses.
It resembles a trumpet,
if a trumpet were a lizard.
The nottle lives above the
tree line in mountainous areas.
To make up for lack of oxygen
the nottle inhales blue skies,
and exhales rain storms.

N is for nottle.

An omple
has coloring like a
skunk and scales
like a fish.
It rolls from place to
place just as a
ball does.

O is for omple.

A plarg is the
only space faring animal
that we know of.
It flaps its enormous albatross
wings until the air is so thin,
it then ignites its high octane
posterior discharge to
escape the atmosphere.
Of course, the plarg has a
little space helmet
on its little head.

P is for plarg.

A qip,
pronounced chip,
resembles a blue bell vine.
Its appearance fools a bee
into thinking it's a flower,
and then the qip
eats the insect.

Q is for qip.

A ronkso
lives on top
of the clouds.
It is rarely seen.
It's an enormous
balloon with tiny
wings like a puffer fish
filled with helium.

R is for ronkso.

A sascadoo is an
aquatic bug that
lives in the shallows,
and looks like a conch.
When you walk
along the beach, and think
you've stepped on a seashell,
you've probably stepped
on a sascadoo.
Its shell opens, and the
sascadoo peeks out.

S is for sascadoo.

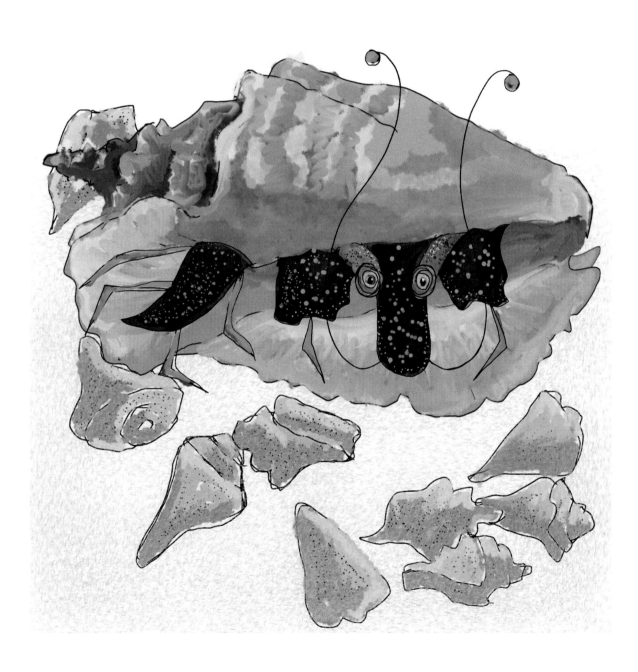

A tallur
is nearly extinct,
because of its prized hide.
This hairy,
long-necked beast lives in
constant paranoia that
people will mistake it for a
sea snake that is in dire
need of a haircut.

T is for tallur.

Ungla is the worst
camouflaged fish,
but its hot pink
and neon green leopard
printed skin is irrelevant,
because it's an
apex predator.
It has three dorsal fins,
eight gills, and large eyes.

U is for ungla.

The vink
is a cute slender little
guy that hops around
in the grass.
It's a deep black,
bipedal, and fluffy
doggish critter.
Its big feet keep it
balanced, and ensure that it
will always land on its feet.

 is for vink.

Werkswill, you'll
never see just one.
They're swarming
creatures, in the
hundreds of thousands.
They're insects you'd
prefer not to encounter.
Werksills live in a hive.

W is for werkswill.

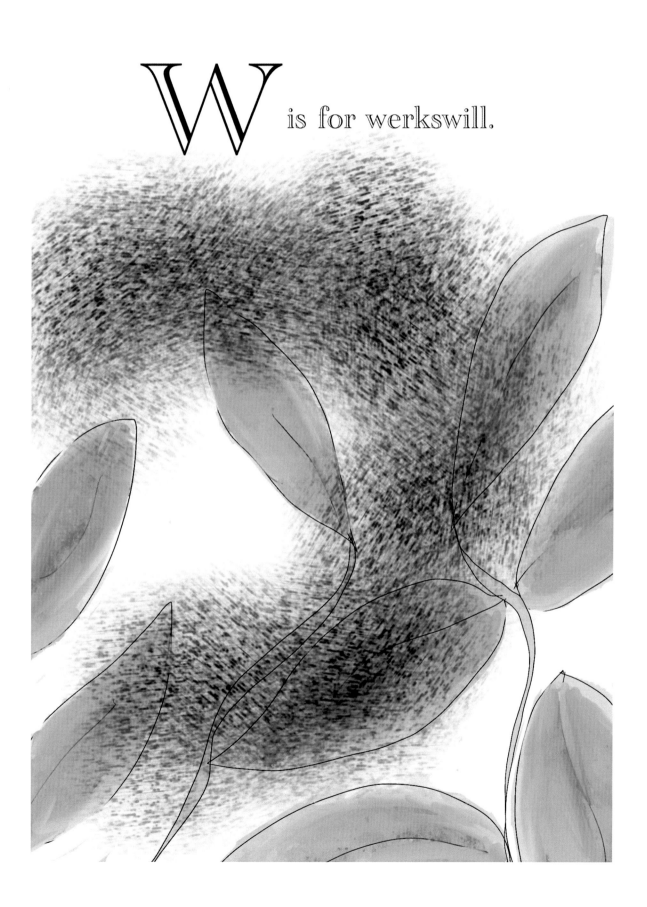

Xanxanthi is an animal that evolved to cuddle up to car engines for warmth. It's mousy and resembles a piston, so it largely goes unnoticed.

X is for xanxanthi.

Yits are mosquitoes,
but tinier and louder.
They swarm into
silhouettes of other
animals such as rabbits.
This attracts
their prey.

Y is for yit.

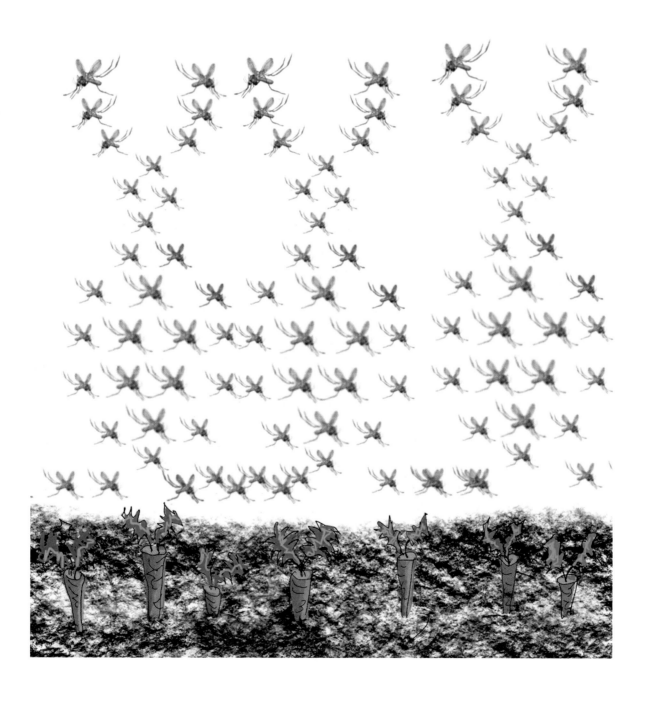

A zonga
is the largest
of the whale family.
Unlike other whales,
the zonga is transparent.
As it swims slowly
along through the deepest
part of the ocean, all you see
is an enormous
skeleton around
the zonga's innards.

Z is for zonga.

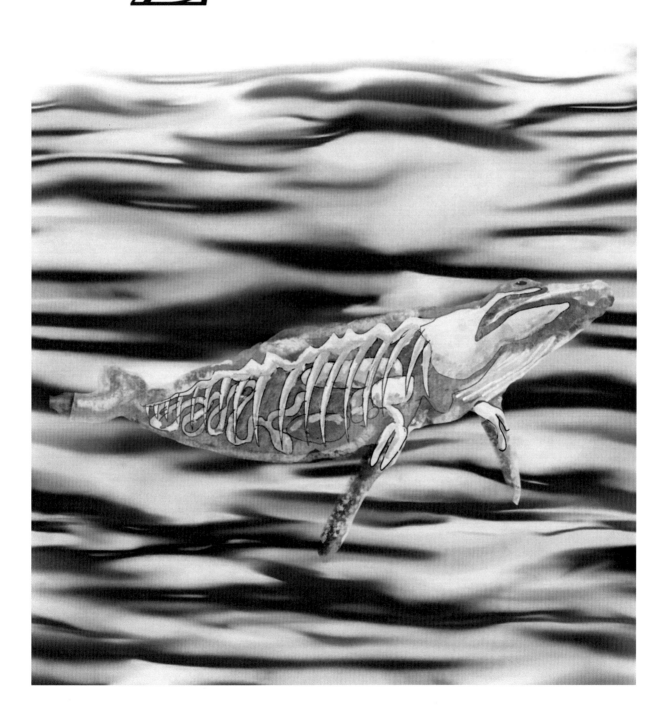

Made in United States
North Haven, CT
15 September 2022

24145125R00031